EASIEST
KEYBOARD
COLLECTION

Christmas

WISE PUBLICATIONS
London/New York/Paris/Sydney/Copenhagen/Madrid

Exclusive Distributors:

Music Sales Limited
8/9 Frith Street,
London W1V 5TZ, England.

Music Sales Pty Limited
120 Rothschild Avenue,
Rosebery, NSW 2018,
Australia.

Order No. AM952105
ISBN 0-7119-7198-6
This book © Copyright 1998 by Wise Publications

Book design by Chloë Alexander
Compiled by Peter Evans
Music arranged by Roger Day
Music processed by Paul Ewers Music Design

Printed in the United Kingdom by
Caligraving Limited, Thetford, Norfolk.

Cover Photograph courtesy of:
Image Bank

Your Guarantee of Quality
As publishers, we strive to produce every book to the highest
commercial standards.
The music has been freshly engraved and the book has been carefully
designed to minimise awkward page turns and to make playing from
it a real pleasure.
Particular care has been given to specifying acid-free, neutral-sized
paper made from pulps which have not been elemental chlorine
bleached. This pulp is from farmed sustainable forests and was
produced with special regard for the environment.
Throughout, the printing and binding have been planned to ensure
a sturdy, attractive publication which should give years of enjoyment.
If your copy fails to meet our high standards, please inform us and
we will gladly replace it.

Music Sales' complete catalogue describes thousands of titles and is
available in full colour sections by subject, direct from Music Sales
Limited. Please state your areas of interest and send a cheque/postal
order for £1.50 for postage to: Music Sales Limited, Newmarket Road,
Bury St. Edmunds, Suffolk IP33 3YB.

Visit the Internet Music Shop at
http://www.musicsales.co.uk

Contents

AWAY IN A MANGER

Traditional Christmas Carol

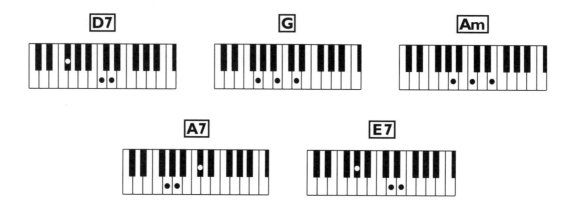

Voice: **Clarinet**

Rhythm: **Waltz**

Tempo: ♩ = 100

A - way in a manger, no crib for a bed, the

lit - tle Lord Je - sus laid down His sweet head. The

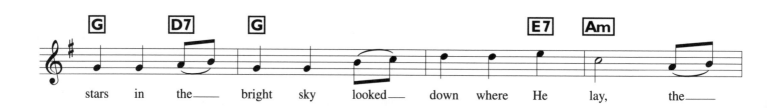

stars in the bright sky looked down where He lay, the

lit - tle Lord Je - sus a - sleep in the hay. The

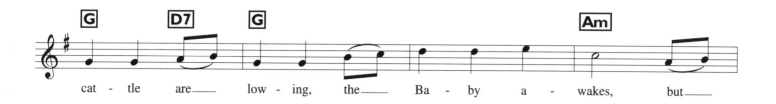

cat - tle are__ low - ing, the__ Ba - by a - wakes, but__

lit - te Lord Je - sus, no__ cry - ing He makes. I

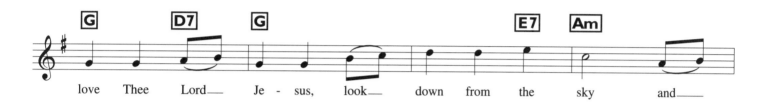

love Thee Lord__ Je - sus, look__ down from the sky and__

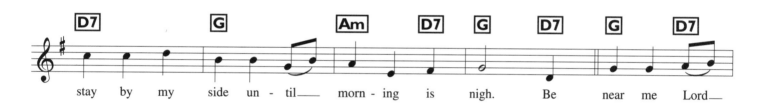

stay by my side un - til__ morn - ing is nigh. Be near me Lord__

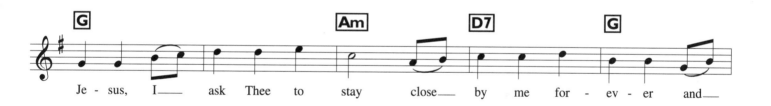

Je - sus, I__ ask Thee to stay close__ by me for - ev - er and__

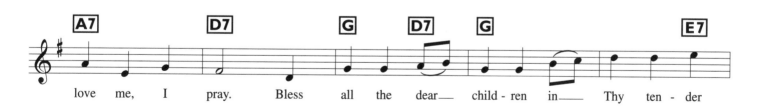

love me, I pray. Bless all the dear__ child - ren in__ Thy ten - der

care, and__ fit us for hea - ven to__ live with Thee there.

DING DONG MERRILY ON HIGH

Traditional
© Copyright 1998 Dorsey Brothers Music Limited, 8/9 Frith Street, London W1.

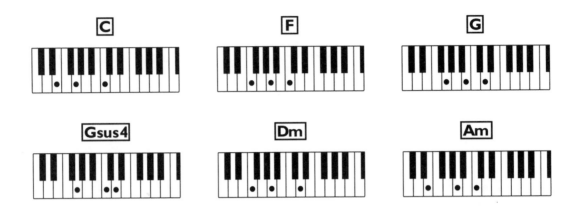

Voice: **Trumpet**

Rhythm: **Soft Rock**

Tempo: ♩ = 146

Ding dong! Mer - ri - ly on high, in heav'n the bells are

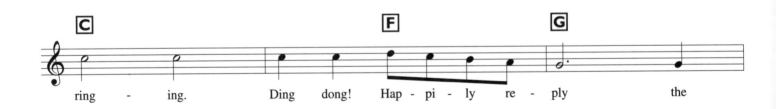

ring - ing. Ding dong! Hap - pi - ly re - ply the

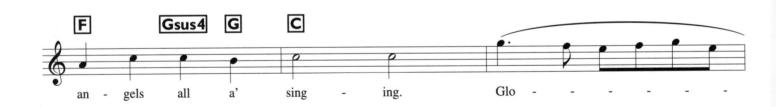

an - gels all a' sing - ing. Glo - - - - -

- - - - -

6

- - - - - - - - ri - a, ho - san - na in ex -

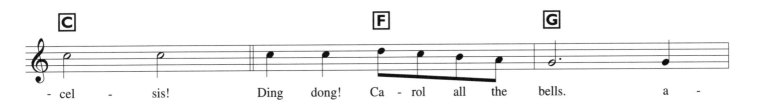

- cel - sis! Ding dong! Ca - rol all the bells. a -

- wake not, do not tar - ry! Sing out, sound the good No -

- wells, Je - su is born of Ma - - - ry.

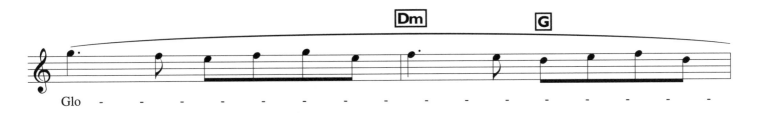

Glo - - - - - - - - - - - - - - - - - -

- - - - - - - - - - - - - - - - - - - -

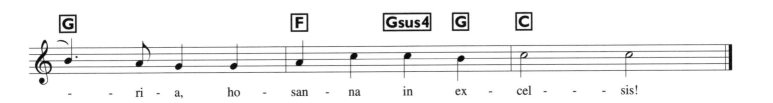

- - ri - a, ho - san - na in ex - cel - - - sis!

FROSTY THE SNOWMAN

Words & Music by Steve Nelson & Jack Rollins
© Copyright 1950 Hill and Range Songs Incorporated, USA.
*Carlin Music Corporation, Iron Bridge House, 3 Bridge Approach, London NW1 for the British Commonwealth
excluding Canada, Australia and New Zealand), Eire and Israel.
All Rights Reserved. International Copyright Secured.*

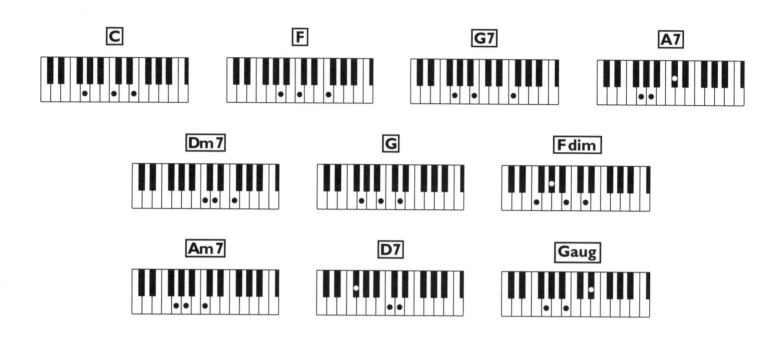

Voice: **Acoustic Guitar**

Rhythm: **8 beat pop**

Tempo: ♩ = 155

Frost - y   the   snow - man   was   a   jol - ly   hap - py

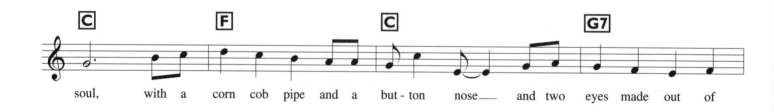

soul,   with a   corn cob pipe and a   but - ton   nose___ and two   eyes made out of

coal.   Frost - y   the   snow - man   is   a   fai - ry   tale, they

say, he was made of snow but the child-ren know—— how he

came to life one day. There must have been some

ma - gic in that old tin hat they found, for

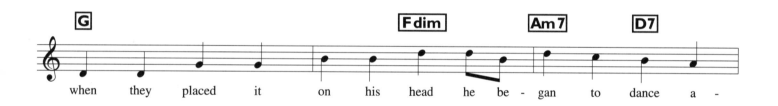

when they placed it on his head he be-gan to dance a -

- round. Oh, Frost - y the snow - man was a -

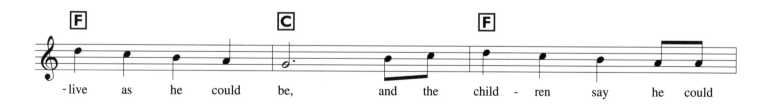

- live as he could be, and the child - ren say he could

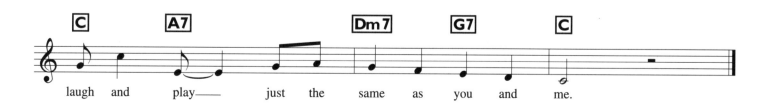

laugh and play—— just the same as you and me.

GOOD KING WENCESLAS

Traditional Christmas Carol
© Copyright 1998 Dorsey Brothers Music Limited, 8/9 Frith Street, London W1.

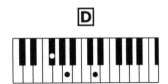
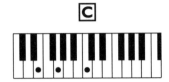
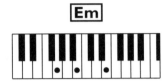

Voice: **Tenor Saxophone**

Rhythm: **Folky Pop**

Tempo: ♩ = 128

Good King Wen - ces - las looked out

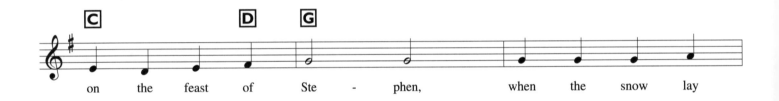

on the feast of Ste - phen, when the snow lay

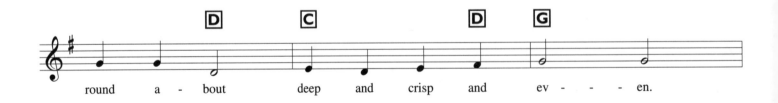

round a - bout deep and crisp and ev - - - en.

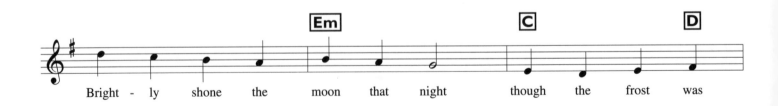

Bright - ly shone the moon that night though the frost was

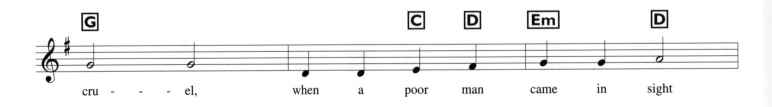

cru - - - el, when a poor man came in sight

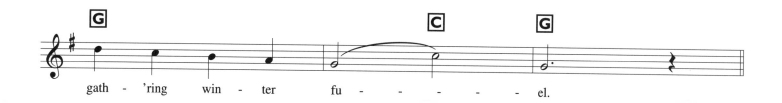

gath - 'ring win - ter fu - - - - - el.

"Hith - er page and stand by me, if thou know'st it

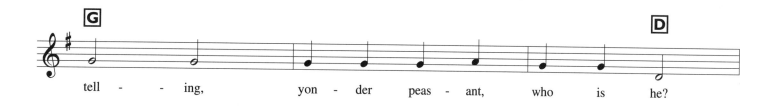

tell - - ing, yon - der peas - ant, who is he?

Where and what his dwell - ing?" "Sire, he lives a

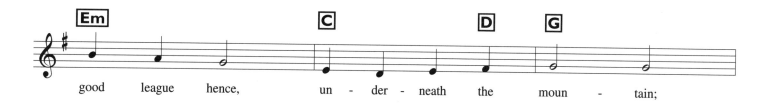

good league hence, un - der - neath the moun - tain;

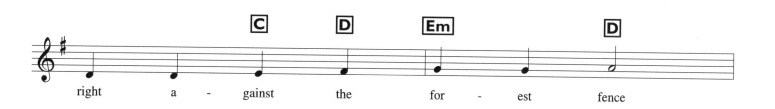

right a - gainst the for - est fence

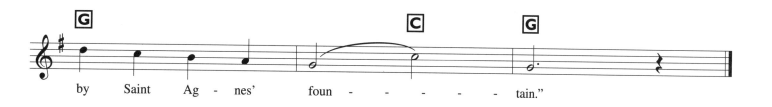

by Saint Ag - nes' foun - - - - - tain."

HAPPY XMAS (WAR IS OVER)

Words & Music by John Lennon & Yoko Ono

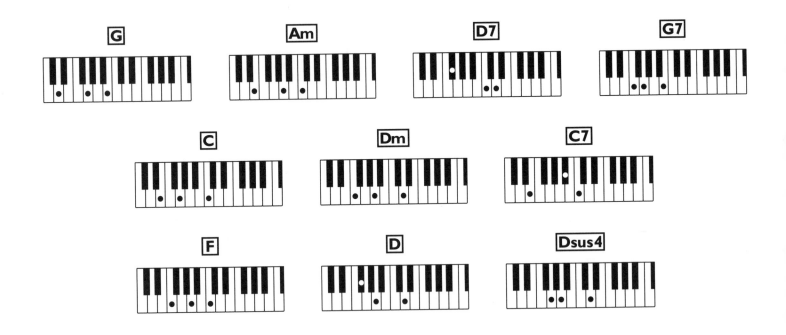

Voice: **Electric Guitar**

Rhythm: **Rock Waltz**

Tempo: ♩ = 148

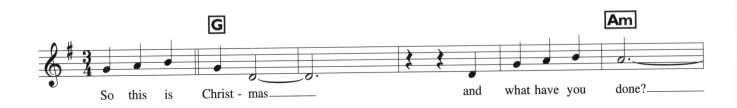

So this is Christ-mas___ and what have you done?___

___ An-oth-er year ov-er,___ a new one just be-

-gun.___ And so this is Christ-mas,___

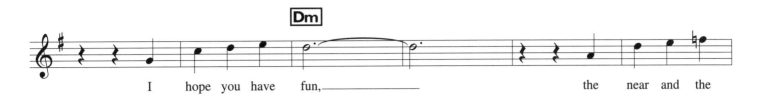

I hope you have fun,_____ the near and the

dear ones,_____ the old and the— young._____

A mer - ry, mer-ry Christ - mas_____ and a hap - py new

year,_____ let's hope it's a good one_____

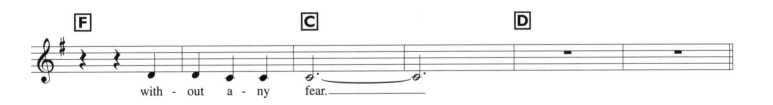

with - out a - ny fear._____

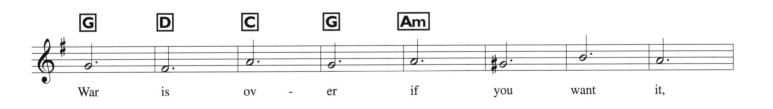

War is ov - er if you want it,

war is ov - er now._____

HARK! THE HERALD ANGELS SING

Christmas Carol
© Copyright 1998 Dorsey Brothers Music Limited, 8/9 Frith Street, London W1.
All Rights Reserved. International Copyright Secured.

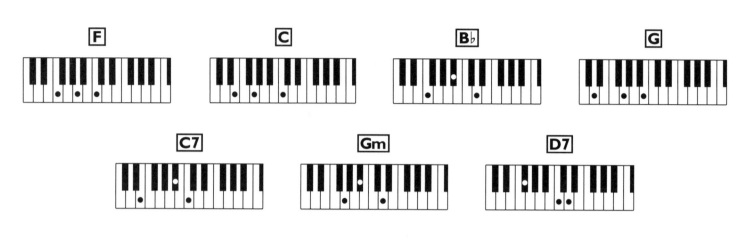

Voice: **Clarinet**

Rhythm: **Folklore**

Tempo: ♩ = 112

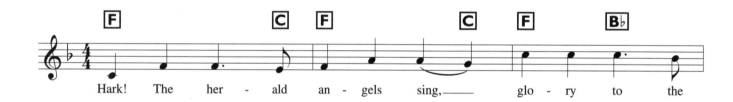

Hark! The her - ald an - gels sing,____ glo - ry to the

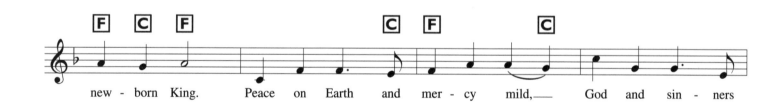

new - born King. Peace on Earth and mer - cy mild,____ God and sin - ners

re - con - ciled. Joy - ful all ye na - tions rise,____ join the tri - umph

of the skies,____ with th'an - ge - lic host pro - claim

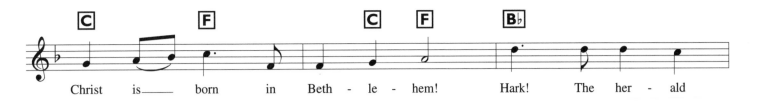

Christ is___ born in Beth - le - hem! Hark! The her - ald

an - gels sing, glo - ry___ to the new - born King!

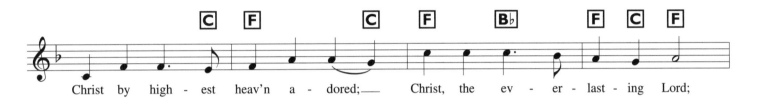

Christ by high - est heav'n a - dored;___ Christ, the ev - er - last - ing Lord;

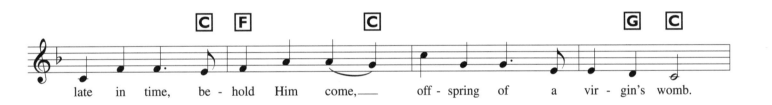

late in time, be - hold Him come,___ off - spring of a vir - gin's womb.

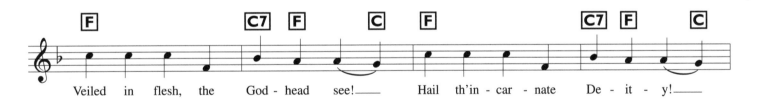

Veiled in flesh, the God - head see!___ Hail th'in - car - nate De - it - y!___

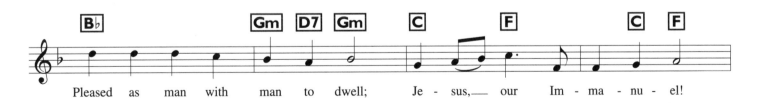

Pleased as man with man to dwell; Je - sus,___ our Im - ma - nu - el!

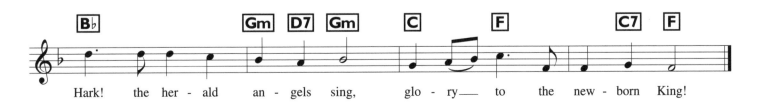

Hark! the her - ald an - gels sing, glo - ry___ to the new - born King!

I SAW THREE SHIPS

Traditional Christmas Carol

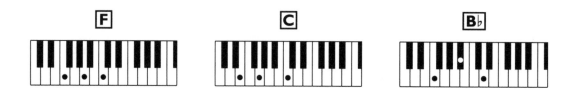

Voice: **Harpsichord**

Rhythm: **Rock Waltz**

Tempo: ♩ = 250

I saw three ships come sail - ing in on

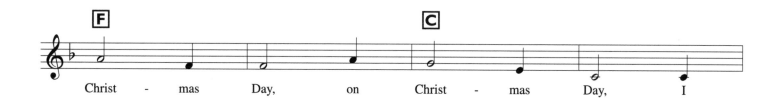

Christ - mas Day, on Christ - mas Day, I

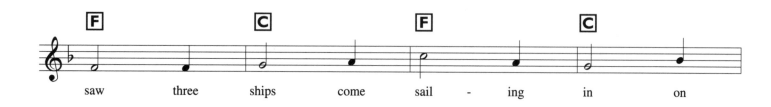

saw three ships come sail - ing in on

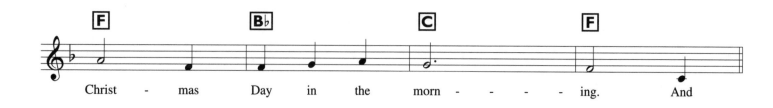

Christ - mas Day in the morn - - - - ing. And

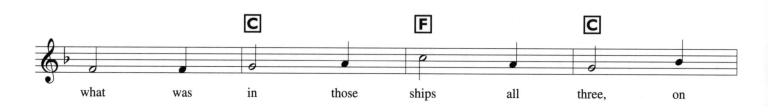

what was in those ships all three, on

I WISH IT COULD BE CHRISTMAS EVERY DAY

Words & Music by Roy Wood

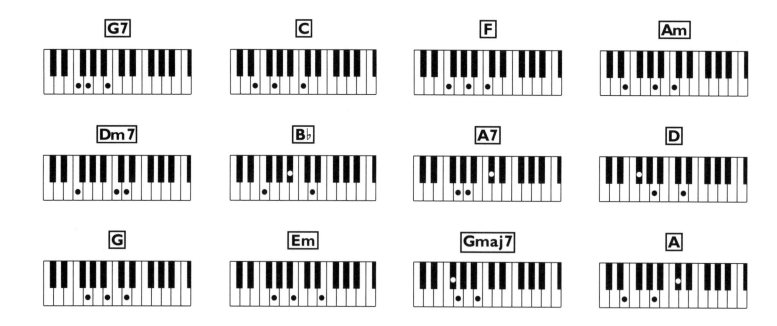

Voice: **Piano**

Rhythm: **Slow Rock**

Tempo: ♩ = 136

Oh when the snow-man brings the snow,— oh well he

just might like to know— he's put a great big smile on some-bo-dy's face.

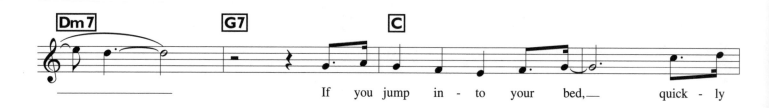

If you jump in-to your bed,— quick-ly

co - ver up your head,___ don't you lock the doors,___ you know that

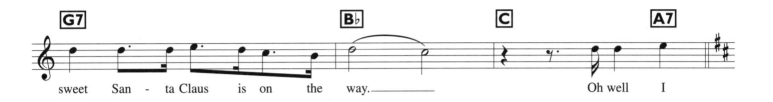

sweet San - ta Claus is on the way.___ Oh well I

wish it could be Christ - mas ev-'ry day,___ when the

kids start sing - ing and the band be - gins___ to play.___ Oh___ I

wish it could be Christ - mas ev-'ry day___ so let the

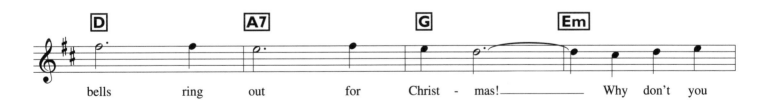

bells ring out for Christ - mas!___ Why don't you

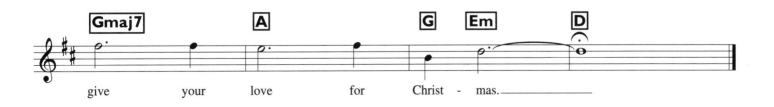

give your love for Christ - mas.___

JINGLE BELLS

Traditional

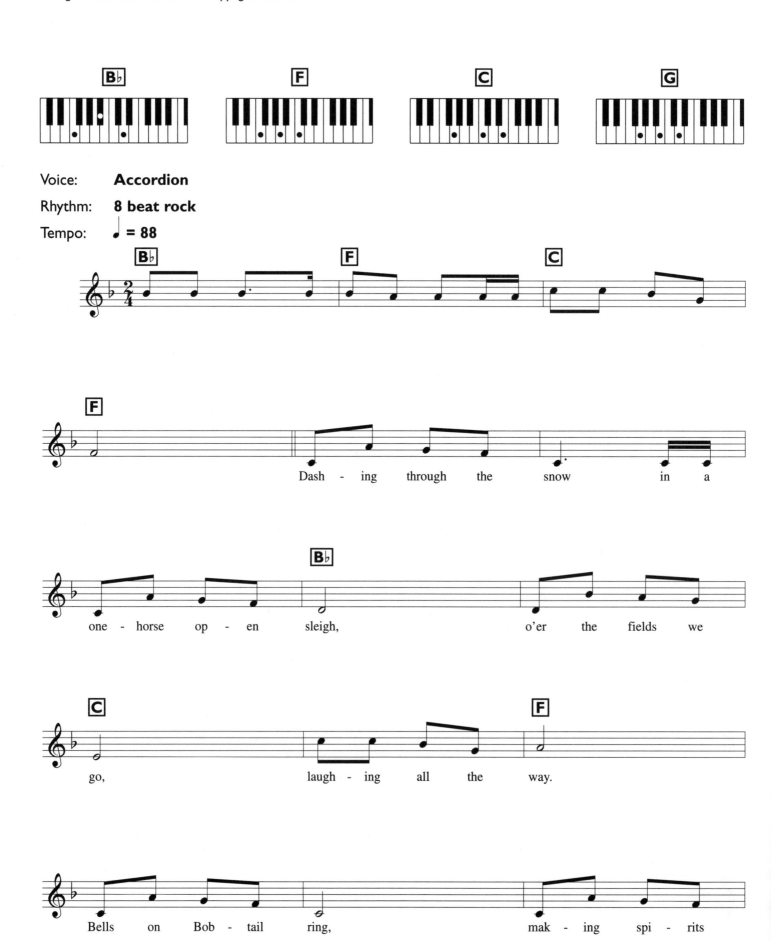

bright,   what   fun   it   is   to   ride   and   sing   a

sleigh - ing   song   to - night.   Jin - gle   bells,

jin - gle   bells.   jin - gle   all   the   way!

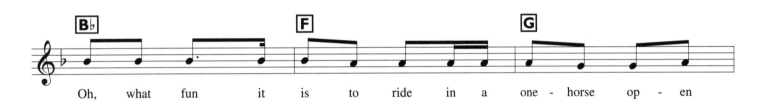

Oh,   what   fun   it   is   to   ride   in   a   one - horse   op - en

sleigh,   hey!   Jin - gle   bells,   jin - gle   bells,

jin - gle   all   the   way!   Oh,   what   fun   it

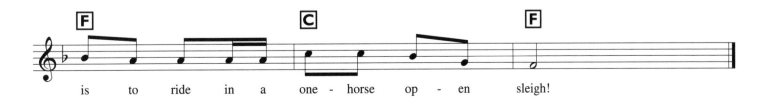

is   to   ride   in   a   one - horse   op - en   sleigh!

LAST CHRISTMAS

Words & Music by George Michael
© Copyright 1985 Morrison Leahy Music Limited, 1 Star Street, London W2.
All Rights Reserved. International Copyright Secured.

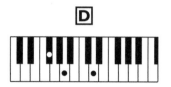 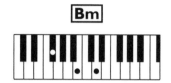 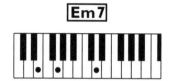 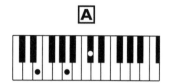

Voice: **Synthetic Bass**

Rhythm: **Soul Ballad**

Tempo: ♩ = 126

Last Christ-mas I gave you my heart— but the ve-ry next day you

gave it a-way.— This year— to save me from tears— I'll

give it to some-one spe-cial. Last Christ-mas I

gave you my heart— but the ve-ry next day you gave it a-way.—

This year— to save me from tears— I'll give it to some-one spe-cial.

Once bit-ten and twice shy,_____ I keep my dis-tance but you still catch_ my eye..

____ Tell me ba - by, do you re-cog-nise me? Well, it's been a year, it

should-n't sur - prise_ me. (*Sp:*) Happy Christmas! I wrapped it up and sent it

with a note_ say-ing "I___ love you," I meant it. Now__ I know__ what a fool__

_____ I've been__ but if you kissed me now__ I know you'd fool me a - gain.__

Last Christ-mas I gave you my heart__ but the ve-ry next day you gave it a-way.__

Repeat to fade

This year__ to save me from tears__ I'll give it to some - one spe - cial.

23

MARY'S BOY CHILD

Words & Music by Jester Hairston

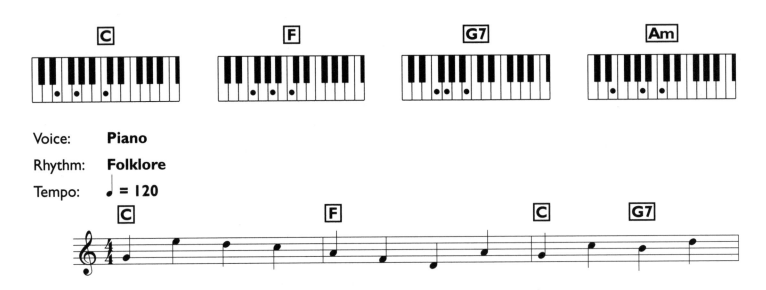

Voice: **Piano**

Rhythm: **Folklore**

Tempo: ♩ = 120

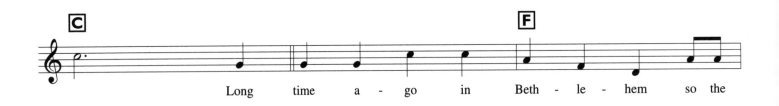

Long time a - go in Beth - le - hem so the

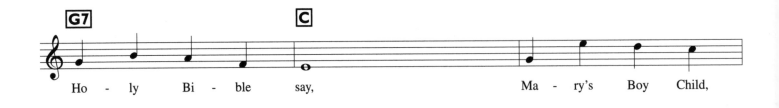

Ho - ly Bi - ble say, Ma - ry's Boy Child,

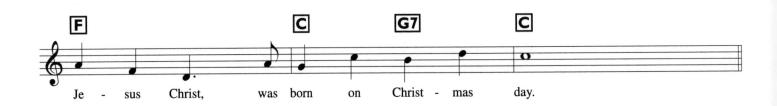

Je - sus Christ, was born on Christ - mas day.

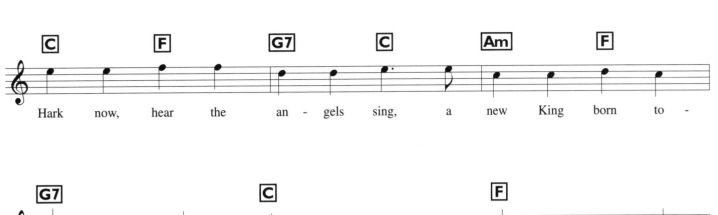

Hark now, hear the an - gels sing, a new King born to -

- day. And man will live for ev - er - more be -

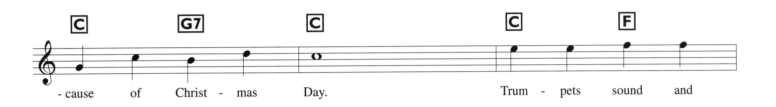

- cause of Christ - mas Day. Trum - pets sound and

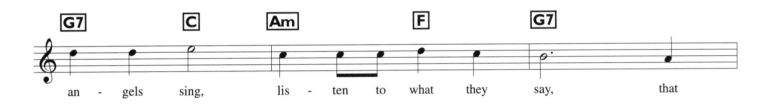

an - gels sing, lis - ten to what they say, that

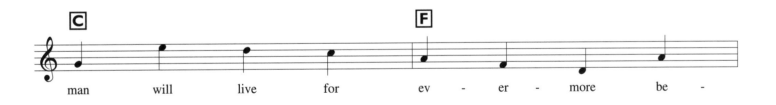

man will live for ev - er - more be -

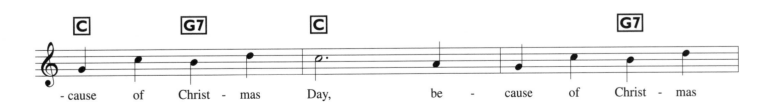

- cause of Christ - mas Day, be - cause of Christ - mas

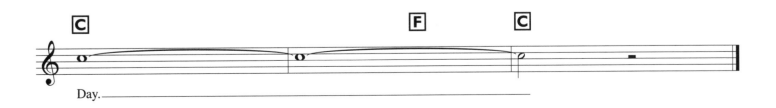

Day.

MERRY XMAS EVERYBODY

Words & Music by Neville Holder & James Lea

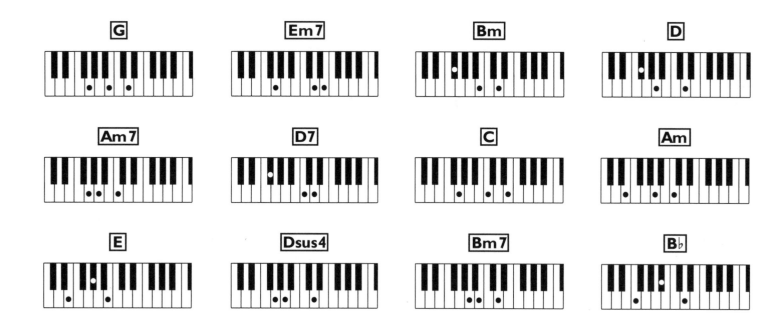

Voice: **Tenor Saxophone**

Rhythm: **Lite Pop**

Tempo: ♩ = 130

Are you hang - - - - ing up a stock -

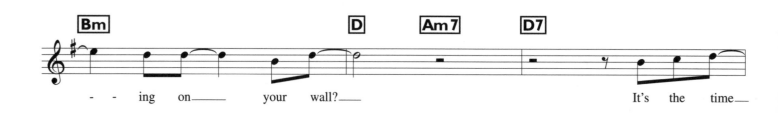

- - - ing on your wall? It's the time

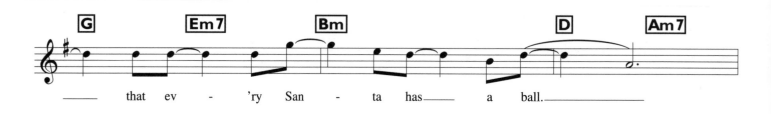

that ev - 'ry San - ta has a ball.

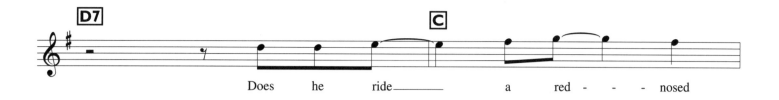

Does he ride_____ a red - - - nosed

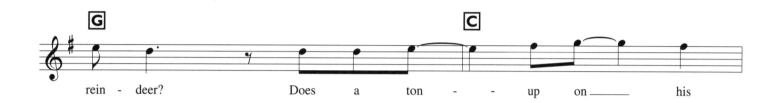

rein - deer? Does a ton - - up on _____ his

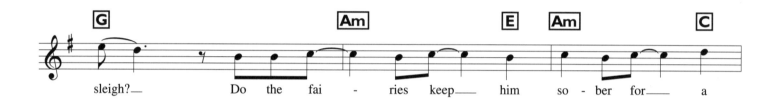

sleigh?_____ Do the fai - ries keep_____ him so - ber for_____ a

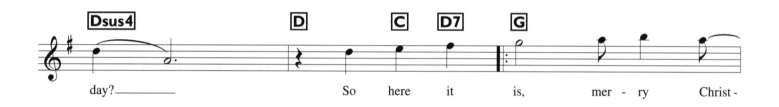

day?_____ So here it is, mer - ry Christ -

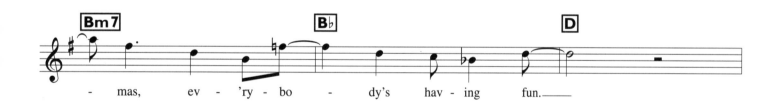

- mas, ev - 'ry - bo - dy's hav - ing fun._____

Look to the fu - ture now,_____ it's on - ly just be -

Repeat to fade

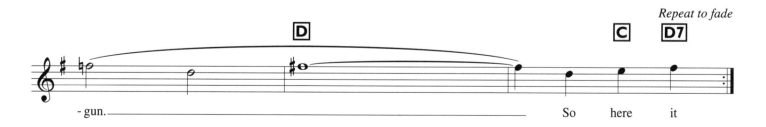

- gun._____ So here it

MISTLETOE AND WINE

Music by Keith Strachan
Words by Leslie Stewart & Jeremy Paul

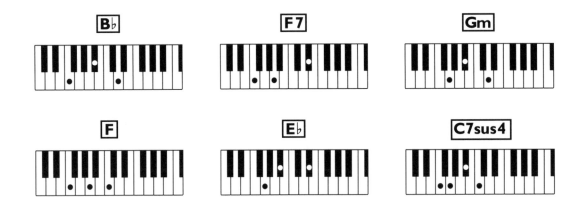

Voice: **Strings**

Rhythm: **Waltz**

Tempo: ♩ = 132

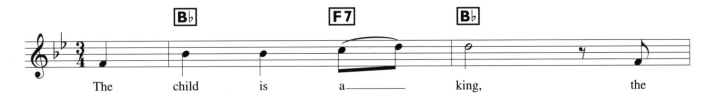

The child is a king, the

ca - rol - lers sing, the old is

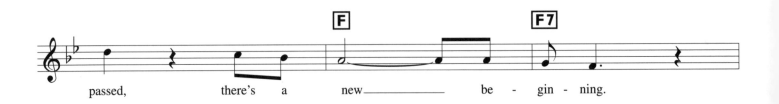

passed, there's a new be - gin - ning.

Dreams of San - ta, dreams of

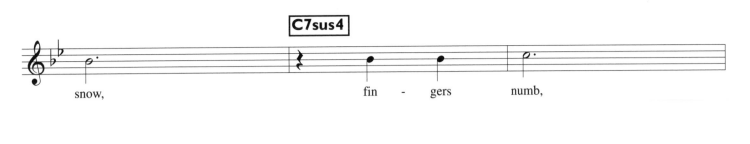

snow, fin - gers numb,

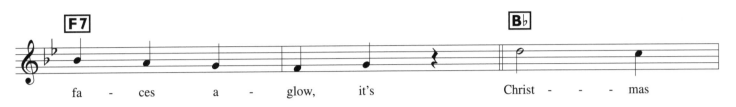

fa - ces a - glow, it's Christ - - - mas

time, mis - tle - toe and wine,

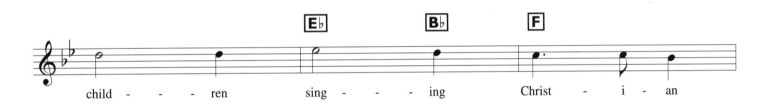

child - - - ren sing - - - ing Christ - i - an

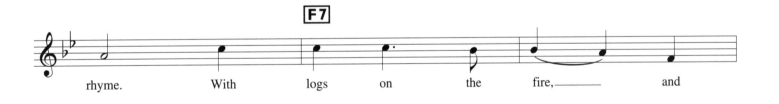

rhyme. With logs on the fire,_____ and

gifts on the tree, a time to re -

- joice in the good that we see.

O COME ALL YE FAITHFUL

Traditional

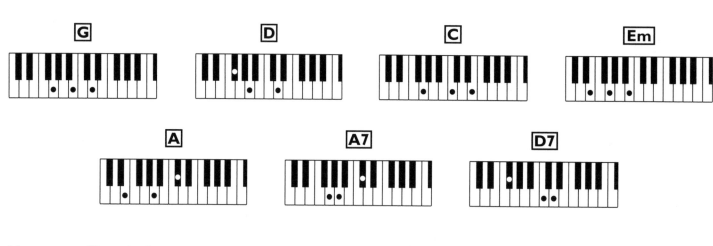

Voice: **Church Organ**

Rhythm: **Soft Rock**

Tempo: ♩ = 112

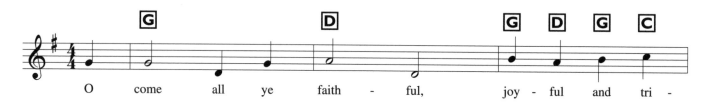

O come all ye faith - ful, joy - ful and tri -

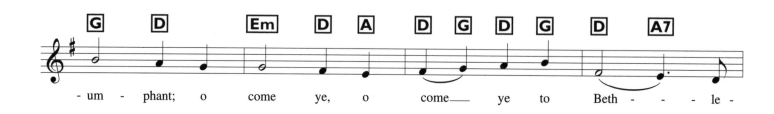

- um - phant; o come ye, o come— ye to Beth - - le -

- hem. Come and be - hold him, born the King of

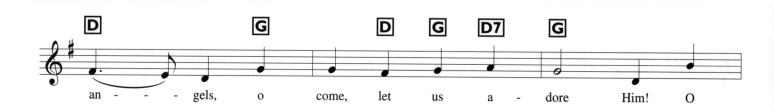

an - - gels, o come, let us a - dore Him! O

come, let us a - dore Him! O come, let us a -

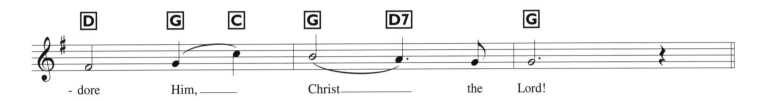

- dore Him, _____ Christ _____ the Lord!

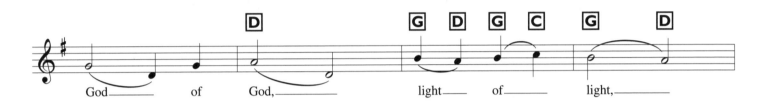

God _____ of God, _____ light _____ of _____ light, _____

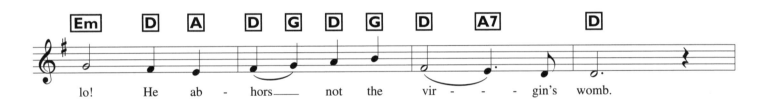

lo! He ab - hors _____ not the vir - - - gin's womb.

Ve - - - ry God, be - got - ten, not cre - a - ted! O

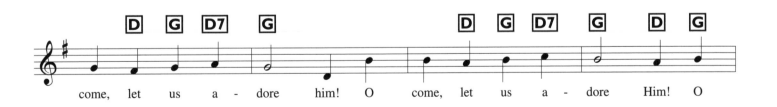

come, let us a - dore him! O come, let us a - dore Him! O

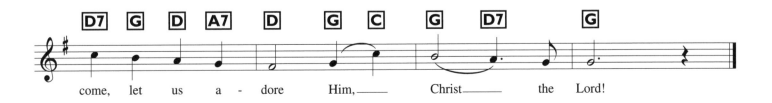

come, let us a - dore Him, _____ Christ _____ the Lord!

O LITTLE TOWN OF BETHLEHEM

Traditional Christmas Carol

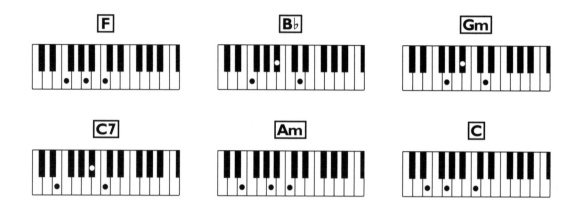

Voice: **Trumpet**

Rhythm: **Folklore**

Tempo: ♩ = 112

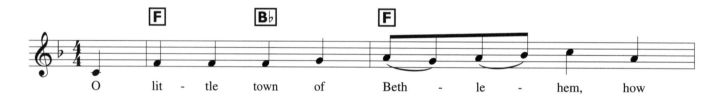

O lit - tle town of Beth - le - hem, how

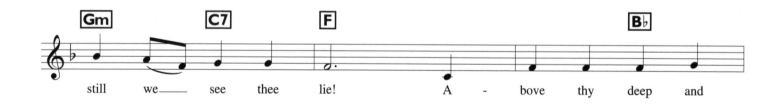

still we___ see thee lie! A - bove thy deep and

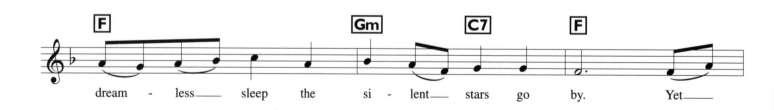

dream - less___ sleep the si - lent___ stars go by. Yet___

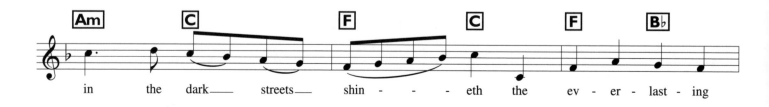

in the dark___ streets___ shin - - - eth the ev - er - last - ing

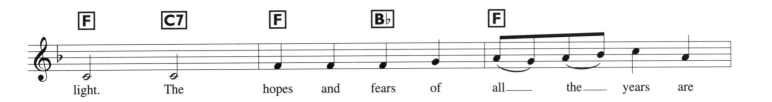

light. The hopes and fears of all___ the___ years are

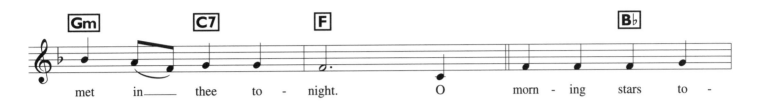

met in___ thee to - night. O morn - ing stars to -

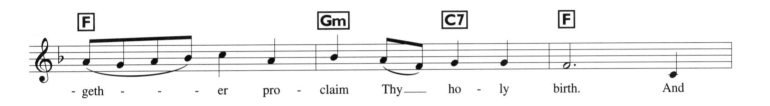

- geth - - - er pro - claim Thy___ ho - ly birth. And

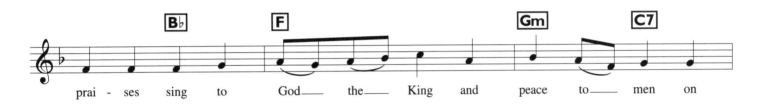

prai - ses sing to God___ the___ King and peace to___ men on

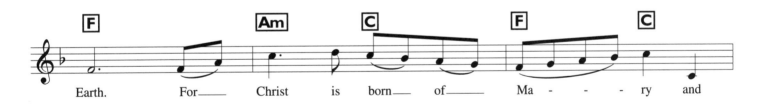

Earth. For___ Christ is born___ of___ Ma - - - ry and

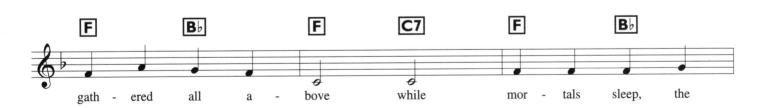

gath - ered all a - bove while mor - tals sleep, the

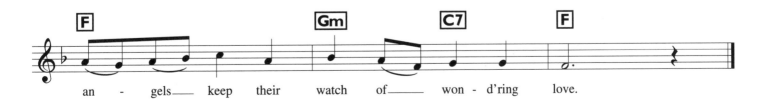

an - gels___ keep their watch of___ won - d'ring love.

ONCE IN ROYAL DAVID'S CITY

Traditional Christmas Carol

 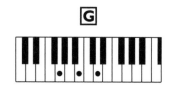 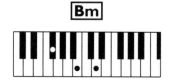 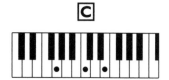

Voice: **Acoustic Guitar**

Rhythm: **Soft Rock**

Tempo: ♩ = 90

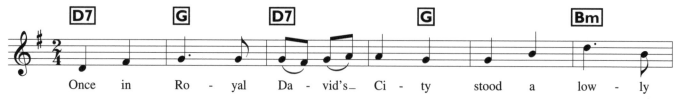

Once in Ro - yal Da - vid's— Ci - ty stood a low - ly

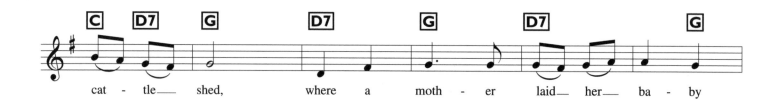

cat - tle— shed, where a moth - er laid— her— ba - by

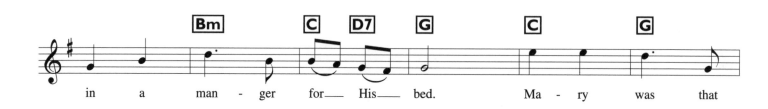

in a man - ger for— His— bed. Ma - ry was that

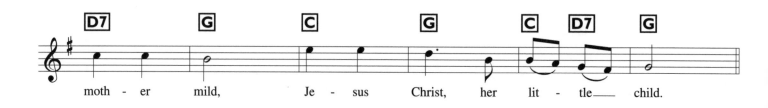

moth - er mild, Je - sus Christ, her lit - tle— child.

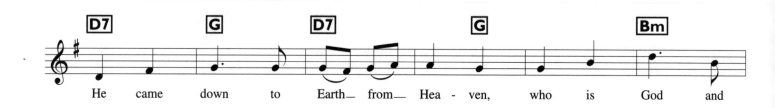

He came down to Earth— from— Hea - ven, who is God and

Lord— of— all. And His shel - ter was— a— sta - ble

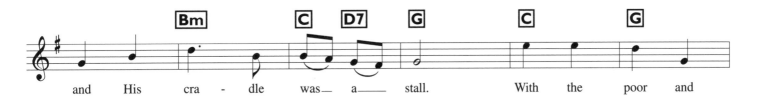

and His cra - dle was— a— stall. With the poor and

mean and low - ly, lived on Earth our Sa - viour— Ho - ly.

And our eyes at last— shall— see him, through His own re -

- deem - ing— love, for that Child so dear— and— gen - tle,

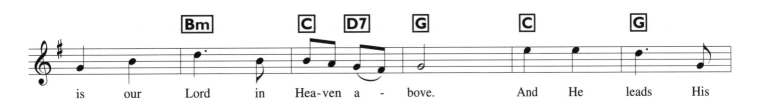

is our Lord in Hea - ven a - bove. And He leads His

child - ren on to the place where He— is— gone.

SILENT NIGHT

Words & Music by Joseph Mohr & Franz Gruber
© Copyright 1998 Dorsey Brothers Music Limited, 8/9 Frith Street, London W1.
All Rights Reserved. International Copyright Secured.

Voice: **Pan Flute**

Rhythm: **Waltz**

Tempo: ♩ = 124

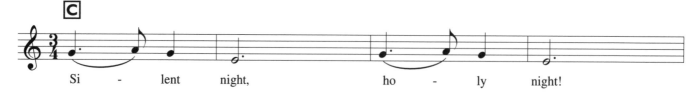

Si - lent night,   ho - ly night!

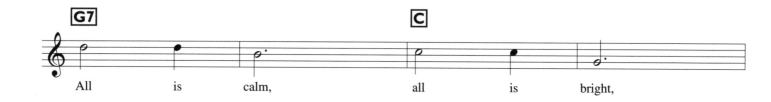

All   is   calm,   all   is   bright,

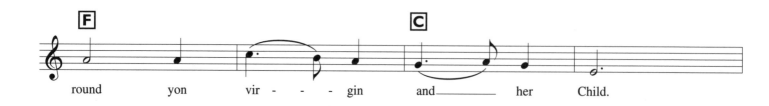

round   yon   vir - - - gin   and⎯⎯ her   Child.

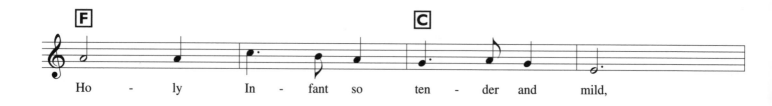

Ho - ly   In - fant so   ten - der and   mild,

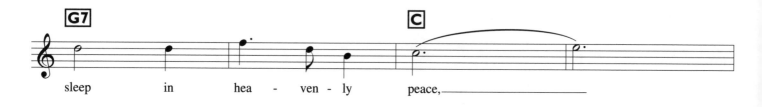

sleep   in   hea - ven - ly   peace,⎯⎯⎯⎯⎯

sleep_____ in hea - ven - ly peace.

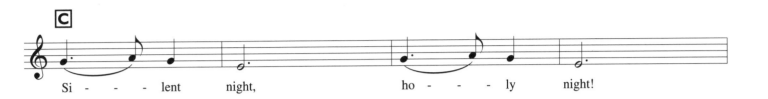

Si - - - lent night, ho - - - ly night!

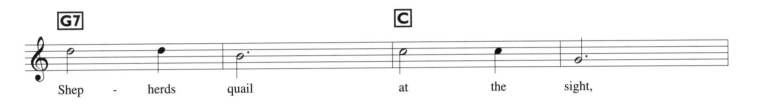

Shep - herds quail at the sight,

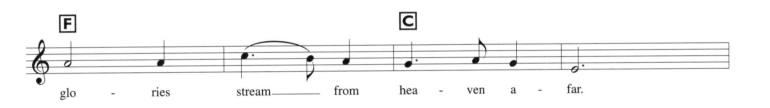

glo - ries stream_____ from hea - ven a - far.

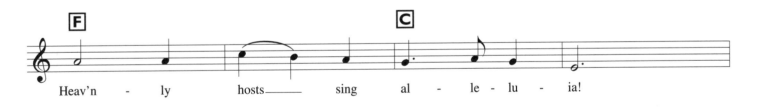

Heav'n - ly hosts_____ sing al - le - lu - ia!

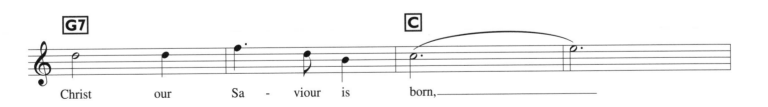

Christ our Sa - viour is born,_____

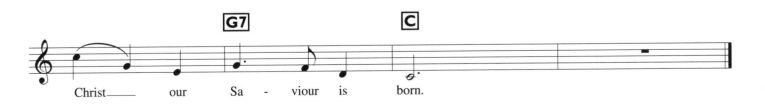

Christ_____ our Sa - viour is born.

WE THREE KINGS OF ORIENT ARE

Traditional

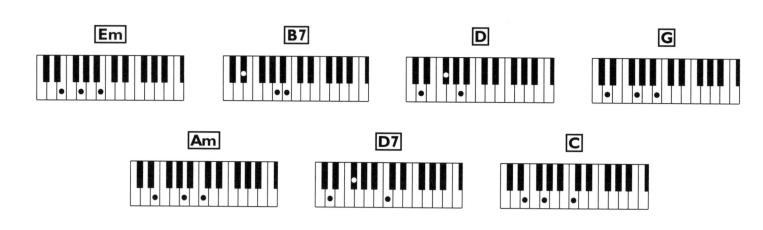

Voice: **Oboe**

Rhythm: **Waltz**

Tempo: ♩ = 174

We three kings of O - ri - ent are, bear - ing

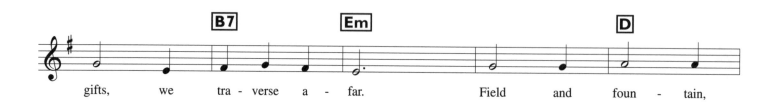

gifts, we tra - verse a - far. Field and foun - tain,

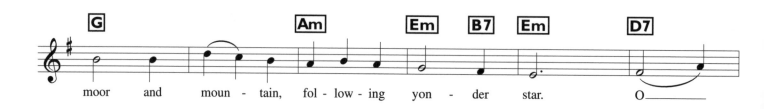

moor and moun - tain, fol - low - ing yon - der star. O————

star of won - der, star of night, star with ro - yal

beau - ty bright, west - ward lead - ing, still pro - ceed - ing,

guide us to thy per - fect light. Born a King on

Beth - le - hem plain, gold I bring to crown Him a - gain.

King for ev - er, ceas - ing ne - ver ov - er us all to

reign. O——— star of won - der, star of night,

star with ro - yal beau - ty bright, west - ward lead - ing,

still pro - ceed - ing. guide us to thy per - fect light.

WE WISH YOU A MERRY CHRISTMAS

Traditional
© Copyright 1998 Dorsey Brothers Music Limited, 8/9 Frith Street, London W1.
All Rights Reserved. International Copyright Secured.

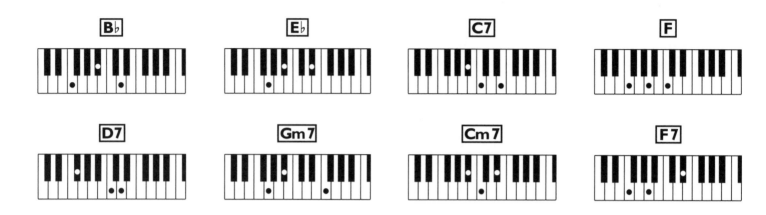

Voice: **Choir**

Rhythm: **Waltz**

Tempo: ♩ = 134

We wish you a mer-ry Christ-mas, we

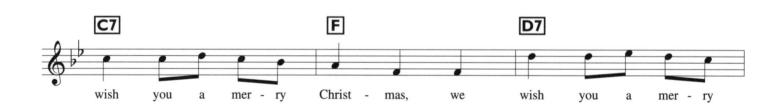

wish you a mer-ry Christ-mas, we wish you a mer-ry

Christ-mas and a hap-py New Year. Good

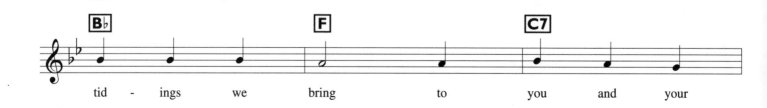

tid-ings we bring to you and your

kin. We wish you a mer - ry Christ - mas and a

hap - py New Year. Now bring us some fig - gy

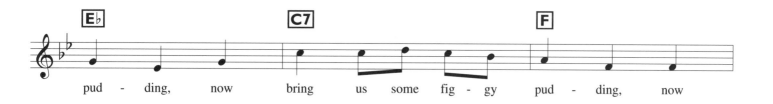

pud - ding, now bring us some fig - gy pud - ding, now

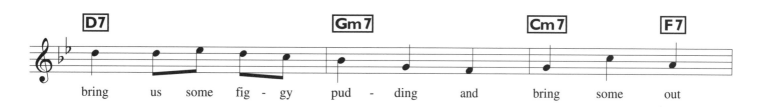

bring us some fig - gy pud - ding and bring some out

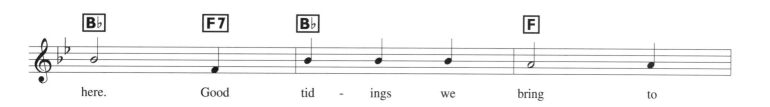

here. Good tid - ings we bring to

you and your kin. We wish you a mer - ry

Christ - mas and a hap - py New Year.

WHILE SHEPHERDS WATCHED THEIR FLOCKS BY NIGHT

Traditional

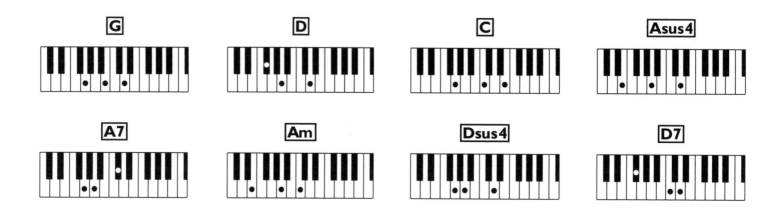

Voice: **Recorder**

Rhythm: **Soft Rock**

Tempo: ♩ = 108

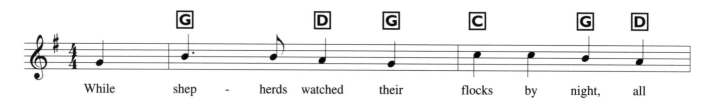

While shep - herds watched their flocks by night, all

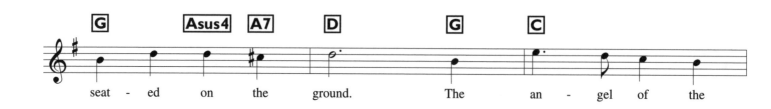

seat - ed on the ground. The an - gel of the

Lord came down and glo - ry shone a - round. "Fear

not!" said he, for might - y dread had seized their trou - bled

mind.   "Glad   tid - ings   of   great   joy   I   bring   to

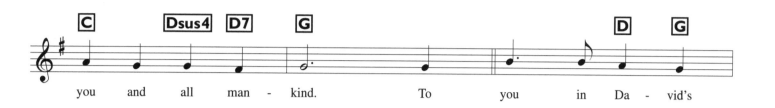

you   and   all   man - kind.   To   you   in   Da - vid's

Town   this   day   is   born   of   Da - vid's   line.   A

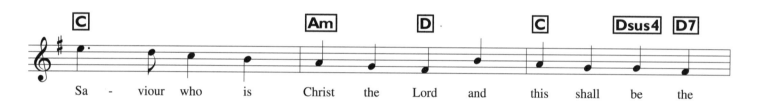

Sa - viour   who   is   Christ   the   Lord   and   this   shall   be   the

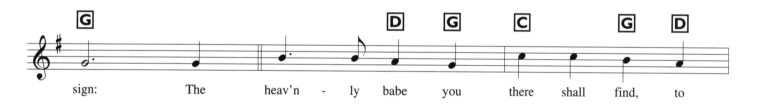

sign: The   heav'n - ly   babe   you   there   shall   find,   to

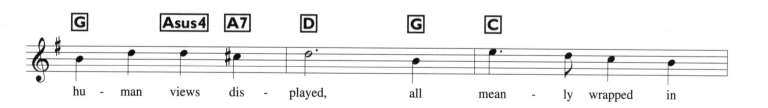

hu - man   views   dis - played,   all   mean - ly   wrapped   in

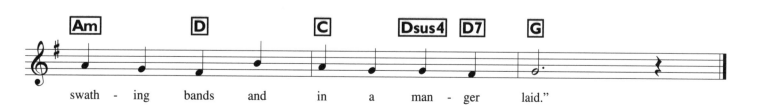

swath - ing   bands   and   in   a   man - ger   laid."

WINTER WONDERLAND

Words by Dick Smith
Music by Felix Bernard

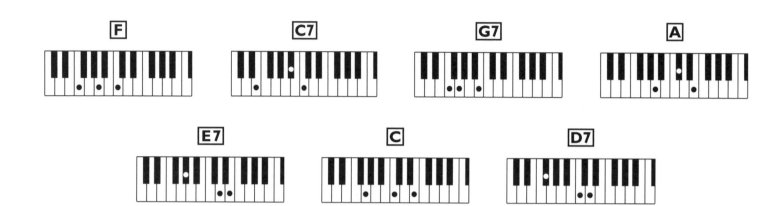

Voice: **Piano**

Rhythm: **Swing**

Tempo: ♩ = 136

Sleigh bells ring, are you list'n-ing? In the lane snow is

glist'n-ing. A beau-ti-ful sight,— we're hap-py to-night,—

walk-ing in a win-ter won-der-land. Gone a-way is the

Blue-bird, here to stay is the new bird; he sings a love song— as

we go a - long, walk - ing in a win - ter won - der - land.

In the mea - dow we can build a snow - man, then pre - tend that he is Par - son

brown. He say "Are you mar - ried?" We'll say "No man! But

you can do the job when you're in town." La - ter

on we'll con - spire as we dream by the

fire, to face un - a - fraid the plans that we made,

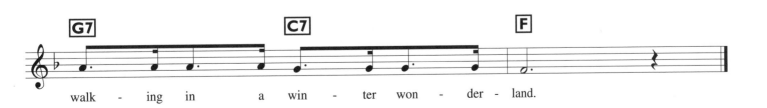

walk - ing in a win - ter won - der - land.

WONDERFUL CHRISTMASTIME

Words & Music by McCartney

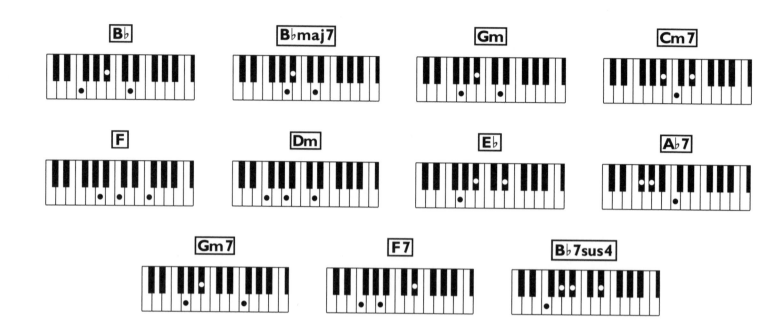

Voice: **Pan Flute**

Rhythm: **Soft Rock**

Tempo: ♩ = 134

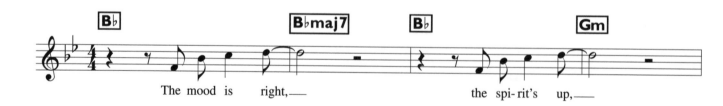

The mood is right,— the spi-rit's up,—

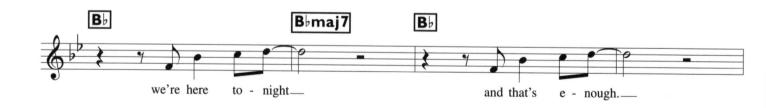

we're here to - night— and that's e - nough.—

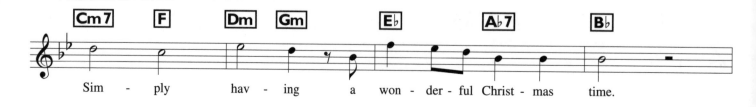

Sim - ply hav - ing a won - der - ful Christ - mas time.

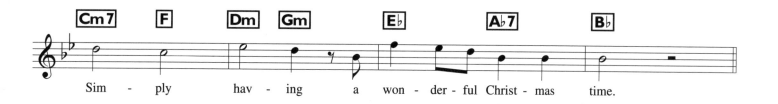
Sim - ply hav - ing a won - der - ful Christ - mas time.

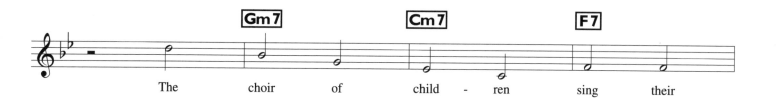
The choir of child - ren sing their

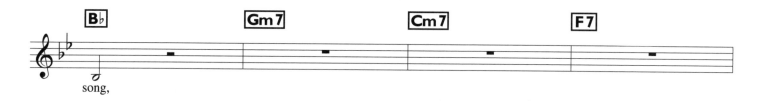
song,

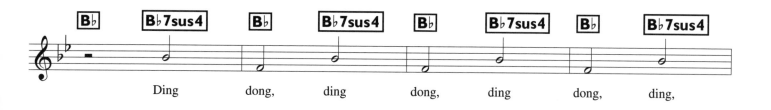
Ding dong, ding dong, ding dong, ding,

ooh, _____ ooh, ___

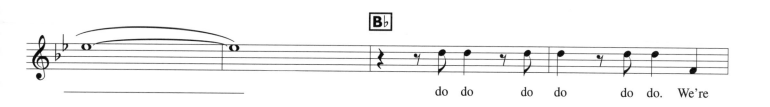
_____ do do do do do do. We're

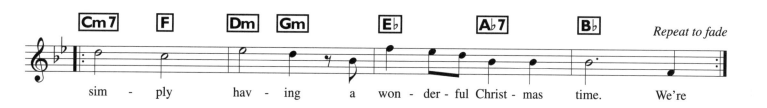
Repeat to fade

sim - ply hav - ing a won - der - ful Christ - mas time. We're

EASIEST KEYBOARD COLLECTION

Easy-to-play melody line arrangements for all keyboards with chord symbols and lyrics. Suggested registration, rhythm and tempo are included for each song together with keyboard diagrams showing left-hand chord voicings used.

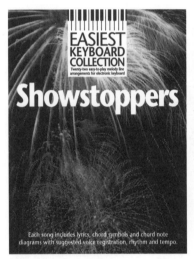  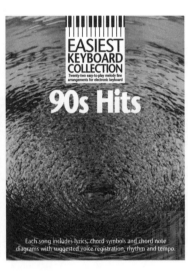 

Showstoppers
Consider Yourself (Oliver!), Do You Hear The People Sing? (Les Misérables), I Know Him So Well (Chess), Maria (West Side Story), Smoke Gets In Your Eyes (Roberta) and 17 more big stage hits.
Order No. AM944218

Pop Classics
A Whiter Shade Of Pale (Procol Harum), Bridge Over Troubled Water (Simon & Garfunkel), Crocodile Rock (Elton John) and nineteen more classic pop hits, including Hey Jude (The Beatles), Imagine (John Lennon), Massachusetts (The Bee Gees) and Stars (Simply Red).
Order No. AM944196

90s Hits
Over twenty of the greatest hits of the 1990s, including Always (Bon Jovi), Fields Of Gold (Sting), Have I Told You Lately (Rod Stewart), One Sweet Day (Mariah Carey), Say You'll Be There (Spice Girls), and Wonderwall (Oasis).
Order No. AM944229

TV Themes
Twenty-two great themes from popular TV series, including Casualty, EastEnders, Gladiators, Heartbeat, I'm Always Here (Baywatch), Red Dwarf and The Black Adder.
Order No. AM944207

Also available...

Film Themes, Order No. AM952050 **Chart Hits**, Order No. AM952083
Jazz Classics, Order No. AM952061 **Classical Themes**, Order No. AM952094
Classic Blues, Order No. AM950697 **Christmas**, Order No. AM952105
Love Songs, Order No. AM950708 **Ballads**, Order No. AM952116
Pop Hits, Order No. AM952072 **Broadway**, Order No. AM952127